Contents

AGES 6–7
KEY STAGE 1

Premier

ar sounds

The letters *ar* make a sound a bit like a pirate!

Learn to recognise words containing the letter blend *ar*. It will help you to read new words.

 Circle all the words in these sentences that use the *ar* blend.

a I hung upside down on the bars in the park.

b Is it far?

c It is really hard to see in the dark!

d My birthday card from Mark was very funny.

e I collected tadpoles in a jar from the pond in my garden.

f When I went into the barn, I saw a rusty old car in the corner.

g My bed is lovely and warm.

h Can't you see how hard this is?

i I got a postcard from Tina!

 Write a word containing *ar* to fill each gap.

a I play on the swings at the _____.

b I spilled blackcurrant and it left a _____ on my clothes.

c The _____ on the trunk of the tree felt very rough.

d As the fire burned, lots of bright _____ flew up in the air.

e My dad drove the _____ down the road.

f My grandma lives really _____ away.

g At night-time, it gets very _____.

h I saw some chickens at the _____.

i The road is covered in black _____.

oy sounds

The sound *oy* is found in many words. So you need to learn to read and spell it. Use **look**, **cover**, **write** and **check**. **Look** at the word and try and make a picture of it in your head. Think of the shape the word makes on the page. Are there any letters with tails (like *y*) or sticks (like *d*)? Then **cover** the words, and try and **write** them. **Check** your spellings with the words on the page.

I Copy out these words. Learn to spell them as you do so. Use look, cover, write, check to help you.

a boy   _____

b toy   _____

c joy   _____

d destroy   _____   g royal   _____

e enjoy   _____   h enjoyed   _____

f annoy   _____   i enjoying   _____

II Write a sentence using each of the words above, to show you understand what they mean.

a _____

b _____

c _____

d _____

e _____

f _____

g _____

h _____

i _____

ow sounds

The sound *ow* is the one we make when we are surprised. It can also be heard in words like thr**ow** and bl**ow**n.

I **Draw lines to match each word to its meaning.**

a crow   The day after today.

b mow   Something to eat soup from.

c bowl   A black bird.

d snow   To cut grass.

e arrow   Where your arm is able to bend.

f elbow   A pointed, wooden stick that is fired from a bow.

g tomorrow   White, cold flakes that fall from the sky.

h grow   To get bigger.

II **Draw a circle around the *ow* words.**
Then write a sentence using each one.

yellow	black	row	race	follow	line	own	face
pillow	bin	slowest	cat	show	marrow	nice	

a _____

b _____

c _____

d _____

e _____

f _____

g _____

h _____

air words

The sound *air* is made by blending the letters *a*, *i* and *r*. In fact, *air* makes a word all by itself. We use it every time we breathe.

I The f*air*y has cast an *air* spell. Write the missing letters in the spaces to make words.

a p_____ed

b h_____

c _____y

d h_____y

e st_____

f f_____

g l_____

h p_____

i f_____y

j f_____est

II Draw a line to match the two sentence halves so they make sense. Each sentence must contain an *air* word!

a Mirror, mirror on the wall

b I put a fairy

c I rode on the dodgems

d I have two black kittens

e Our kitchen is light and airy

f The princess marched bravely

g I walked up the stairs

h I screamed when I saw

i I brush my hair

j On the school trip

into the dragon's lair.

so that makes a pair!

when I went to the fair.

who is the fairest of them all?

to make myself neat and tidy.

to go to bed.

at the top of the Christmas tree.

a big hairy spider.

because it has large windows that open.

my teacher paired me up with my best friend.

or blends

There are lots of words that contain the blend *or*. So it is a very useful sound blend to be able to read and spell.

I The words under these boxes all use the *or* blend. Draw each thing described.

a
cork

c
cord

e
storm

b
torch

d
horse

f
fork

II Colour in the storm clouds that contain *or* words.

form

purse

sport

afford

turkey

snort

next

scorch

smoke

morning

night

port

north

porch

worn

shed

er sounds

The sound *er* is very common. That means we see it a lot! Sometimes *er* is found in the middle of a word, but often it is found at the end of a word.

supp**er**

teach**er**

 Draw lines to join each *er* word to its matching picture.

a herb

b letter

c butter

d pepper

e winter

f slipper

g summer

h numbers

i river

II **Look at each *er* word. Then write a sentence that contains it.**

a hotter _____

b fatter _____

c smaller _____

d sharper _____

e bigger _____

f wider _____

g colder _____

h smellier _____

i sillier _____

ear words

ear is a word all by itself, but the letter blend can also be found in lots of other words.

pear

fear

Draw a pearl shape round all the *ear* words. Then write them in the spaces below.

hear	tearing	bare	tear	fear	fair	wear
smear	bear	bowl	pearl	heard	herd	

a _____   d _____   g _____

b _____   e _____   h _____

c _____   f _____   i _____

Help the bear collect the honey pots with *ear* words inside. Colour them in, then write the words below.

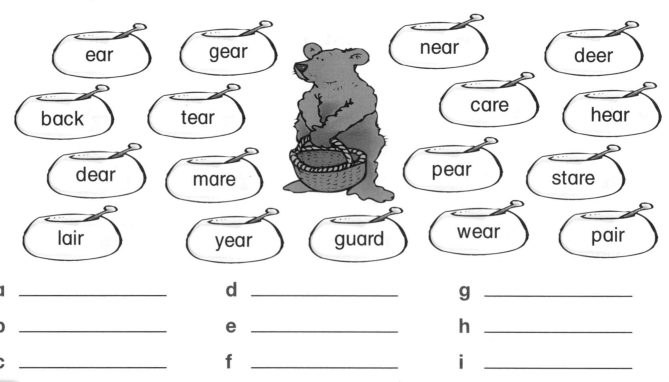

a _____   d _____   g _____

b _____   e _____   h _____

c _____   f _____   i _____

8

ea words

We find the *ea* blend in lots of words.

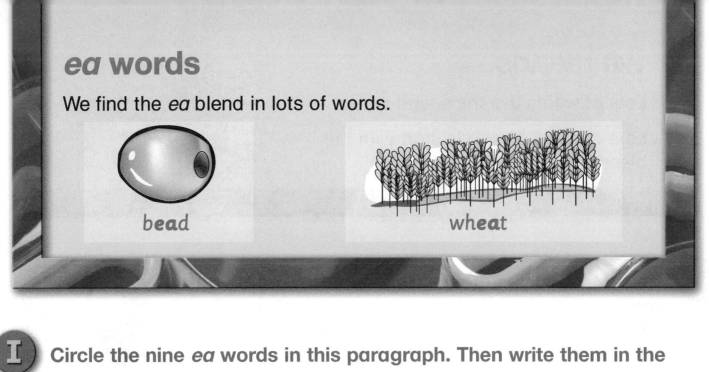

bead

wheat

I   Circle the nine *ea* words in this paragraph. Then write them in the spaces.

I sat on the seat to eat my tea. I looked at the sea as I ate my pie and peas, followed by peaches and cream. Then I washed my sticky face clean and started to read.

a _____   d _____   g _____

b _____   e _____   h _____

c _____   f _____   i _____

II   Write a story that uses all of these *ea* words and tick them off the list as you use them.

_____

_____

_____

_____

_____

_____

_____

_____

_____

_____

weak	☐
mean	☐
leaf	☐
search	☐
sea	☐
team	☐
fear	☐
beach	☐
beat	☐
beak	☐

wh blends

Lots of words use the sound **wh**oo!

Lots of question words start with the blend *wh*.

I) This little ghost is making the sound whoo! He has found a set of cards with *wh* words on. Colour in the card in each set that contains the blend *wh*.

a | wheel | wink | water |

b | wait | white | wellington |

c | whale | wall | watch |

d | will | whisk | weight |

e | wham | winkle | witch |

f | win | whimper | wand |

g | wind | swim | whisper |

h | wag | while | west |

) Make up questions, using each of these words that begin with *wh*.

| what   who   where   when   which   why |

a _____

b _____

c _____

d _____

e _____

f _____

ch blends

Do you prefer **ch**ips or **ch**ocolate? They are both tasty and they both start with the letter blend *ch*.

II The words under these boxes all use the *ch* blend. Draw a picture of these things.

a

chick

c

lunch

e

chin

b

chimp

d

child

f

chip

I Underline the *ch* blends in each word. Then write a sentence using that word.

a chill _____

b much _____

c chest _____

d rich _____

e check _____

f such _____

g bench _____

h bunch

Breaking words down

When you spell words, it is useful to break them into smaller chunks. This helps when you are reading, too.

Drawing could be easily broken into dr-aw-ing.

I **Break these words into small chunks. Then learn to spell them.**

a **snail**   breaks down into   _____-_____

b **writing**   breaks down into   _____-_____

c **hotel**   breaks down into   _____-_____

d **maybe**   breaks down into   _____-_____

e **donkey**   breaks down into   _____-_____

f **flowers**   breaks down into   _____-_____

g **carrot**   breaks down into   _____-_____

h **important**   breaks down into   _____-_____-_____

i **computer**   breaks down into   _____-_____-_____

II **Write the missing chunks of each word. Use the words in the box to help you.**

| because |
| brother |
| sister |
| would |
| jump |
| should |
| jumping |
| another |

a sh-_____-ld

b br-_____-er

c be-cau-_____

d w-_____-_____

e j-_____-_____

f _____-um-_____

g sis-_____

h an-_____-_____

Verbs

Verbs are the action words in a sentence. They tell you what is being done. Some people call them '**doing words**'.

Lick is a **verb**. It tells us what is being done.

 Underline the verbs in each sentence.

a The bird flew away.

b The girl laughed at her brothers.

c The mother ate a big slice of cake.

d The snake slid across the rocks.

e The lion roared.

f The two brothers were shouting very loudly!

g The mouse squeaked as it ran.

h The sun shone brightly.

i I ran down the street.

 Complete each sentence with a verb that makes sense. Use the words in the box to help you.

a The giraffe _____ leaves from high branches.

b The dog _____ at the postman.

c My dad _____ very loudly!

d The teacher _____ her name on the board.

e The spider _____ in the corner.

f The horse _____ away.

g The cat _____ because it was happy.

h The waves _____ up the beach.

Verbs
snores
purred
roared
ate
wrote
galloped
barked
lurked

Tenses

The words we write tell us whether things are happening now, in the past or in the future.

I am walking is the **present** – now.

I walked   is in the **past**.

I shall walk   is in the **future**.

 Write down whether these sentences are in the past, present or future tense.

a I sat on the chair.   _____

b I went to the party.   _____

c I'll see you in the
   morning.   _____

d She saw a cat.   _____

e I shall go to school
   tomorrow.   _____

f I am laughing.   _____

g I can see a rainbow!   _____

h I ran all the
   way home.   _____

i I am reading a
   great story.   _____

j I am swimming.   _____

 Cross out the wrong verb tense in each sentence.

a I **wented went** to school today.

b I **seen saw** a whale!

c Did you **see saw** that sunset?

d Who **ran runned** the fastest?

e I **won winned** the race!

f I **catched caught** the ball.

g He **seed saw** the film today.

h I **goed went** to my Granny's yesterday.

i I **caught catched** a cold.

j Who **wented went** to the park this morning?

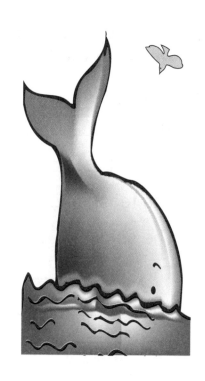

Vowels and consonants

Vowels are the letters **a e i o u**

Consonants are the other letters in the alphabet:
b c d f g h j k l m n p q r s t v w x y z

Most English words contain at least one vowel:
Man sit cake

Y is a strange letter, because it can act like a vowel.

Y acts like a vowel in some words: Fly cry my

I **Fill in the vowels to complete these words.**

a c __ ll __ d

b l __ k __

c s h __ __ l d

d b __ c __ __ s e

e m __ y b __

f s __ s t __ r

g b r __ t h __ r

h w __ __ l d

i w h __ t

j c __ __ l d

II **Make as many three letter words as you can by putting different vowels in the spaces. The first one has been started for you.**

a c __ t   _cat_ _____

b p __ n   _____

c b __ n   _____

d d __ g   _____

e b __ g   _____

f h __ t   _____

g d __ d   _____

h p __ t   _____

i b __ d   _____

j l __ p   _____

Compound words

Compound words are made from smaller words joined together, without changing the spelling.

butter + fly = butterfly

I Draw a line to match the parts of the compound words to make new words.

a news   lid

b sand   castle

c flower   bird

d lady   pot

e eye   paper

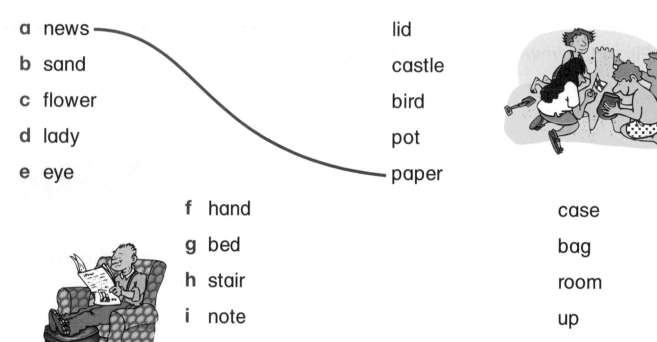

f hand   case

g bed   bag

h stair   room

i note   up

j make   book

II Use the words in the box to make 10 compound words.

all	crow	fish	board	stick	day	bull	skate	stack	week

a scare _____

b _____ board

c star _____

d cup _____

e hay _____

f birth _____

g _____ dog

h lip _____

i _____ end

j over _____

Syllables

Syllables are the **chunks of sound** that make up words. If you say words out loud, you can hear the syllables.

bathroom has two syllables:
bath + room

crocodile has three syllables:
croc + o + dile

Count the syllables in each word. Then write the answer in the box.

a caterpillar ☐

b leaf ☐

c garden ☐

d rainbow ☐

e spider ☐

f butterfly ☐

g ladybird ☐

h bird ☐

i hedgehog ☐

j greenhouse ☐

Rewrite the words in order, with the words with the lowest number of syllables first.

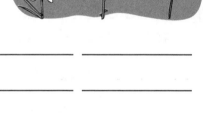

a daisy rose buttercup _____ _____ _____

b chinchilla cat rabbit _____ _____ _____

c planet sun universe _____ _____ _____

d sausages eggs bacon _____ _____ _____

e orange banana lime _____ _____ _____

f pen pencil computer _____ _____ _____

g telephone mobile talk _____ _____ _____

h tea chocolate coffee _____ _____ _____

i sandwiches cake trifle _____ _____ _____

j scorpion ant beetle _____ _____ _____

Synonyms

Synonyms are words that mean the same, or nearly the same, thing.

Sad and unhappy are synonyms.

 I Match the synonyms with a line.

a	insects	flame
b	larger	toss
c	near	bugs
d	small	fastest
e	shining	bigger
f	throw	close
g	shout	tiny
h	quickest	sparkling
i	fire	yell

II Read each sentence. Then circle the answer that has almost the same meaning as the bold word.

a That is a **huge** dog!   enormous   small   scary

b The boy **pushed** the bike out of the way.   raced   shoved   changed

c I **like** sweets.   eat   enjoy   hate

d The girls **laughed** at the joke.   smiled   frowned   giggled

e The lion **ran** quickly.   sprinted   skipped   walked

f The man **drank** his lemonade.   spilled   tipped   swigged

g The lady **sobbed** because she was sad.   cried   frowned   sighed

h The stars **shone** in the sky.   hung   stood   twinkled

Homophones

Homophones are words that sound the same even if they have a different meaning or spelling. Homophones may also be spelled the same, such as bear (animal) and bear (carry or put up with).

An example would be:

two *the number 2*
too *as well*
to *as in going to*

 Draw a line to match the homophones.

a isle   pear

b allowed   beach

c ate   deer

d I   bare

e bear   I'll

f beech   eye

g pair   eight

h creek   creak

i dear   aloud

 Cross out the homophone in each sentence that does not make sense.

a My auntie said I had **grown groan** since she last saw me.

b My **hare hair** is blonde.

c Can I come **two too**?

d A **herd heard** of sheep ran towards me.

e The **hole whole** class said hello.

f **Our Hour** cat likes fish.

g I **know no** your name.

h I **moan mown** if I have toothache.

Suffix *ly*

In this sentence, the word **carefully** is an adverb. It tells how the girl made the model. The *ly* at the end is a **suffix**, added to the word **careful**. By adding *ly* we make an adverb that tells us how something happens or is done.

The girl made the model plane **carefully**.

I Complete each sentence with the correct adverb from the box.

happily kindly lazily delicately roughly selfishly sadly

a The swimmer rubbed herself _____ with the towel.

b The boy _____ shared his sweets.

c The cat stretched out _____ on the chair.

d My grandma smiled _____ when she saw me coming.

e The man frowned _____.

f The butterfly fluttered _____ from flower to flower.

g The boy _____ said he would not share his toys.

II Match the adverb to the correct description.

a carefully   shining

b bravely   fast

c brightly   done with care

d beautifully   not afraid

e perfectly   not done well

f quickly   moving in a delicate way

g badly   done in a lovely way

h gracefully   absolutely correct

Suffix *ful*

The letters *ful* can be added to the end of words as a *suffix*. When you add the suffix *ful* to a word, you are saying that it is **full of** something.

A spoon**ful** of sugar is a spoon **full of** sugar.

 Write the new word, using the suffix *ful*, in the space.

a Full of hope [hope + ful] = _____

b Full of joy [joy + ful] = _____

c Full of peace [peace + ful] = _____

d Full of sorrow [sorrow + ful] = _____

e Full of colour [colour + ful] = _____

f Full of doubt [doubt + ful] = _____

g Full of cheer [cheer + ful] = _____

h Full of power [power + ful] = _____

i Full of thought [thought + ful] = _____

 Write out the meaning of each word.

a wonderful _____

b playful _____

c useful _____

d helpful _____

e hopeful _____

f joyful _____

g truthful _____

h beautiful _____

i hateful _____

Using an index

An index is found in some **non-fiction** books. It helps readers to find information they need. It is in alphabetical order so it is easy to find things.

 I Look at this index. Write down which page numbers you need to look at to find out more.

Apples 67, 71

Cats 16, 18, 90

Frost 24, 43

Nests 15

a To read about apples, I would find pages [ ].

b To read about cats, I would find pages [ ].

c To read about nests, I would find page [ ].

d To read about frost, I would find pages [ ].

II This index has been mixed up. Rewrite it in the correct order. Remember, it should be alphabetical.

goldfish 26

snail 31

water 76

shrew 31, 66

gnat 22

moth 54

iris 12

bat 1, 14

worm 42, 59

willow 37

a _____

b _____

c _____

d _____

e _____

f _____

g _____

h _____

i _____

j _____

Tricky spellings

Some words do not seem to follow spelling rules or are difficult to work out by saying out loud. You just have to learn them by heart.

every	gnat	neither

 Here are some tricky words. Write them out, then try to learn them. Use look, cover, write, check to learn.

a only _____

b little _____

c down _____

d their _____

e because _____

f could _____

g would _____

h should _____

i does _____

j goes _____

II **Spend a few minutes looking at each word. Cover it up. Then try to write it from memory. Check your spelling against the original.**

a mother _____

b father _____

c always _____

d once _____

e upon _____

f after _____

g every _____

h eight _____

i brother _____

j before _____

Time words

Words can be used to show when something happens.

next   after   before   during

I Complete each sentence using a word from the box. You may use the words more than once.

next   after
before   during

a Snow had fallen _____ the night.

b I brush my teeth _____ I go to bed.

c _____ school, I have a swimming lesson.

d _____ dinner, I often have some ice cream.

e I have eaten a lolly and _____ I would like a bag of crisps.

f _____ we went to the cinema, we went shopping because we had seen an advertisement for cheap videos before the film.

g We had our dinner _____ we went out so we would not be hungry.

h _____ I was born, my mum and dad lived in the town.

II Now write two sentences using each time word below.

before   a _____

b _____

after   c _____

d _____

during   e _____

f _____

next   g _____

h _____

firstly   i _____

j _____

Writing stories

Do you like writing stories? There are things you need to remember if you want to make your stories exciting:

- an exciting beginning to tempt the reader to continue

- descriptions of where the story happens

- interesting descriptions of characters

- exciting dialogue – what the characters say.

I **You are going to write a story. First, imagine what your characters are like and make them seem real!**

a What do they look like? _____

b What are their clothes like? _____

c What are their voices like? _____

d How do they walk? _____

e Do they have a favourite food? _____

f How do they act with their friends? _____

g Do they have a problem to solve, or a challenge to face?

_____

II **Now make notes about where your story is set. Use your senses and imagine you are there. Then write your story!**

a Where is your story set? _____

b What can you see? _____

c Can you smell anything? _____

d Describe how things feel – like rough tree bark or a cold window.

_____

e Can you hear anything? _____

f Can you taste anything – like a salty sea breeze? _____

Commas in a list

When you make a list of things in a sentence, you should separate them with commas and put the word 'and' between the last two things on the list.

I bought some eggs, potatoes, carrots, bananas and peppers.

  Add commas in the correct place for each sentence.

a I like cats dogs and rabbits.

b I read books comics and newspapers.

c My favourite foods are cake toast and oranges.

d I collected shells stones and seaweed to decorate my sandcastle.

e Rainbows are red orange yellow green blue indigo and violet.

f It is cold so put on a hat scarf and gloves.

g I drink orange juice cola and milk.

h I saw tigers lions and hippos at the zoo.

  Make up sentences of your own about these things. Include lists and don't forget the commas.

a animals _____

b games _____

c clothes _____

d toys _____

e vegetables _____

f plants _____

g bugs _____

h sports _____

Questions

Question marks show when a question has been asked.

Are we there yet?

Special question words also give us clues that questions are being asked:

Why   Where

When   What

Who   Which   How

Add the question marks to these sentences.

a What is your name

b 'Can I come too ' asked Mary.

c Why can't I That's not fair!

d Would you like a sweet

e Why not I want to!

f Do you like snakes

g Do you want to come with me I don't mind.

h Can we go today

i Who was that

j Would anyone like some supper

Choose a word from the box to make each sentence make sense. You can use the words more than once.

why	where	when	what	who

a _____ said that?

b _____ are my keys?

c _____ is your name?

d _____ did you do that?

e _____ time is it?

f _____ is my pen?

g _____ can we go to the park?

h _____ would like to play with me?

i _____ shall we go shopping?

j _____ would you like to drink?

Writing *ai, ar, un*

It is important to practise your handwriting, so that people can read all the good things you write about!

ai   ar   un

I Copy these words to practise joining *a* and *i*.

a airy _____

b brain _____

c drain _____

d fairy _____

e air _____

f train _____

g fair _____

h chair _____

i dairy _____

j chain _____

II Now copy these *ar* and *un* words.

a shark _____

b dark _____

c bark _____

d car _____

e bar _____

f bun _____

g fun _____

h under _____

Writing *ou, vi, wi*

Some letters have horizontal joins.

ou, vi and *wi* are examples.

ou vi wi

I Copy the *ou* words.

a you _____

b could _____

c would _____

d should _____

e mouth _____

f youth _____

g bought _____

h fought _____

i drought _____

j found _____

II Now copy the *vi* and *wi* words.

a vitamin _____

b vine _____

c wink _____

d win _____

e wind _____

f visit _____

g video _____

h wife _____

Writing *ab, ul, it*

Some handwriting patterns are difficult, because they join a small letter to a tall letter.

ab ul it

I Now copy the words.

a about _____

b baby _____

c table _____

d able _____

e cable _____

f dab _____

g rabbit _____

h habit _____

i label _____

j tabby _____

II Now copy these *ul* and *it* words.

a full _____

b bit _____

c bite _____

d hit _____

e bull _____

f kite _____

g lit _____

h pull _____

Writing *ol, wh, ot*

These handwriting joins are quite tricky, but the more you practise, the easier it will become.

ol wh ot

I **Copy these words in your best handwriting.**

a hot _____

b why _____

c when _____

d which _____

e who _____

f otter _____

g other _____

h got _____

i dot _____

j what _____

II **Now copy these words.**

a doll _____

b hold _____

c fold _____

d mole _____

e sold _____

f told _____

g golly _____

h lolly _____

ANSWERS

Page 2

I
- a bars, park
- b far
- c hard, dark
- d card, Mark
- e jar, garden
- f barn, car
- g warm
- h hard
- i postcard

II
- a park
- b mark
- c bark
- d sparks
- e car
- f far
- g dark
- h farm
- i tarmac

Page 3

I Words learned with correct spellings.

II Any sentences containing the words. Samples shown below.
- a The boy played in the park.
- b My teddy is my favourite toy.
- c I jumped for joy when I scored a goal.
- d The dog will destroy my homework if she gets hold of it!
- e I enjoy cake.
- f Flies annoy me.
- g A queen is royal.
- h I enjoyed your party!
- i I am enjoying this film.

Page 4

I
- a A black bird.
- b To cut grass.
- c Something to eat soup from.
- d White, cold flakes that fall from the sky.
- e A pointed, wooden stick that is fired from a bow.
- f Where your arm is able to bend.
- g The day after today.
- h To get bigger.

II Circled: yellow, pillow, row, slowest, follow, show, marrow, own.
Any sentences containing the words which show the child understands the meaning of each word.

Page 5

I
- a paired
- b hair
- c airy
- d hairy
- e stair
- f fair
- g lair
- h pair
- i fairy
- j fairest

II
- a who is the fairest of them all?
- b at the top of the Christmas tree.
- c when I went to the fair.
- d so that makes a pair!
- e because it has large windows that open.
- f into the dragon's lair.
- g to go to bed.
- h a big hairy spider.
- i to make myself neat and tidy.
- j my teacher paired me up with my best friend.

Page 6

I Pictures of:
- a cork
- b torch
- c cord
- d horse
- e storm
- f fork

II Coloured in: form, afford, north, snort, scorch, porch, worn, sport, morning, port

Page 7

I Pictures matched to correct word.

II Any sentences that make sense and contain the er words. Examples given below:
- a My tea is hotter than I can bear!
- b My cat is fatter than my dog.
- c My sister is smaller than her friends.
- d My nails are sharper than needles!
- e My house is bigger than yours.
- f This river is wider than the River Tyne.
- g It feels much colder today.
- h This sock is smellier than mine!
- i You are sillier than my brother!

Page 8

I hear, smear, tearing, bear, tear, pearl, fear, heard, wear

II Coloured in: ear, dear, gear, tear, year, near, pear, wear, hear

Page 9

I
- a seat
- b eat
- c tea
- d sea
- e peas
- f peaches
- g cream
- h clean
- i read

II A story containing all of the ea words in the box.

Page 10

I
- a wheel
- b white
- c whale
- d whisk
- e wham
- f whimper
- g whisper
- h while

II Any questions using what, who, where, when, which, why.
For example: What is the time?
Who is that? Where are we? When will we go out? Which cake is mine?
Why are you late?

Page 11

I Pictures of:
- a chick
- b chimp
- c lunch
- d child
- e chin
- f chip

II Any sentences that make sense and contain the given words.
- a chill
- b much
- c chest
- d rich
- e check
- f such
- g bench
- h bunch

Page 12

I There is no right way to segment these words; your child should break them down in any way that makes them easy to remember. Here are some suggestions:
- a sn - ail
- b writ - ing
- c ho - tel
- d may - be
- e don - key
- f flow - ers
- g car - rot
- h imp - ort - ant
- i com - put - er

II
- a ou
- b oth
- c se
- d ou - ld
- e ump - ing
- f j - p
- g ter
- h oth - er

Page 13

I
- a flew
- b laughed
- c ate
- d slid
- e roared
- f shouting
- g squeaked
- h shone
- i ran

II
- a ate
- b barked
- c snores
- d wrote
- e lurked
- f galloped
- g purred
- h roared

Page 14

I
- a past
- b past
- c future
- d past
- e future
- f present
- g present
- h past
- i present
- j present

II Cross out:
- a wented
- b seen
- c saw
- d runned
- e winned
- f catched
- g seed
- h goed
- i catched
- j wented

Page 15

I
- a called
- b like
- c should
- d because
- e maybe
- f sister
- g brother
- h would
- i what
- j could

II
- a cat, cut, cot
- b pan, pen, pin, pun
- c ban, Ben, bin, bun
- d dig, dog, dug
- e bag, beg, big, bog, bug
- f hat, hit, hot, hut
- g dad, did, dud
- h pat, pet, pit, pot, put
- i bad, bed, bid, bud
- j lap, lip, lop